Contents

Special Features

Features

When It Is
Night

Written by Cory Winesap

"When it is night,
I get up," said the owl.

"When it is night,
I get up," said the bat.

"When it is night,
I get up," said the hippo.

"When it is night,
I get up," said the lion.

"When it is night,
I get up," said the chipmunk.

"When it is night,
I get up," said the frog.

"When it is night,
I get up," said the moon.

I Like to Bike

Written by Simone Santo
Illustrated by Carol Herring

bike
hike
like
Mike
spike
strike
bike
hike
like
Mike
spike
strike
bike
hike
like
Mike
spike
strike

bike
hike
like
Mike
spike
strike
bike
hike
like
Mike
spike
strike
bike
hike
like
Mike
spike
strike

When it's day,
I ride my bike.
When it's day,
I like to bike.
When it's night,
It's sleep I like.

Day and Night

Written by Harry Chan

Day

The sun comes up.

Night

The sun goes down.

Day

The sky is blue.

Night

The sky is black.

Day

The children are awake.

Night

The children are asleep.

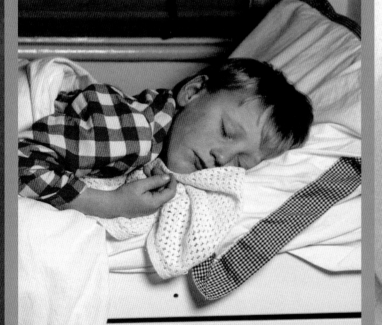

I Like Day

Written by Krystal Diaz
Illustrated by Irma Le Roux

Boy

Cat

Dog

Girl

Boy

I like day.

In the day, I like to run.

Girl

I like day.

In the day, I like to jump.

Dog

I like day.

In the day, I like to chase cats.

Cat

I like day.

In the day, I like to chase birds.

Boy
I like night.
At night, I like to read books.

Girl
I like night.
At night, I like to watch TV.

Dog
I like night.
At night, I like to chew a bone.

Cat
I like night.
At night, I like to purr.

Boy
At night,
I like to go to sleep.

Girl
At night,
I like to go to sleep.

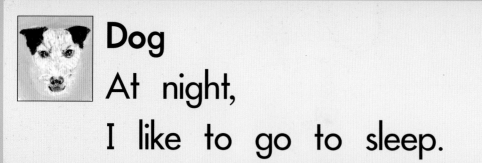 **Dog**
At night,
I like to go to sleep.

 **Cat**
At night,
I like to go to sleep.

Twinkle,Twinkle, Little Star

Traditional

Twinkle, twinkle, little star,
How I wonder what you are,
Up above the world so high,
Like a diamond in the sky.

readingsafari.com

Check out these Safari magazines, too!

Have your say -

e-mail your Safari Tour Guide at
tourguide@readingsafari.com

Safari Tour Guide,   🌵 40

I wrote a story about day and night.
Do you want me to send it to you?

Caitlin Glynn (6)

Find some fun things to do!

Go to –
http://www.readingsafari.com

Safari Superstar

Name – Lion

Birthday – November 12

Find out more about this Safari Superstar at
http://www.readingsafari.com